IMPROVING PROBLEM-SOLVING SKILLS

for ages 7-8

Andrew Brodie

Contents

	Page
Introduction	3
The Steps to Success	4
Ants and spiders: counting strategies, comparing numbers, more, fewer, addition, subtraction, multiplication, division	5-8
Neighbours: comparing ages, odd numbers, even numbers	9-12
I think of a number: addition and subtraction	13-16
I think of a number: multiplication and division	17-20
Collecting cards: comparing and combining two-digit numbers	21-24
How much change?: finding change when buying one or more items costing less than £1	25-28
What time is it?: finding times given by adding or subtracting time durations	29-32
What time is it?: roman numerals; finding times given by adding or subtracting time durations	33-36
Months of the year: time, ordinal number	37-40
Pictogram: interpreting data	41-44
Information in tables: interpreting data	45-48
Planks of wood: comparing and combining lengths	49-52
Picture tiles: multiplication and division, measurement	53-56
Sweets in jars: comparing estimates to actual results; adding, subtracting and sharing	57-60
Comparing numbers: one-digit, two-digit and three-digit numbers	61-64

Andrew Brodie: Improving Problem-solving Skills for ages 7-8 © Bloomsbury Publishing Plc 2013

Introduction

How to use the book and CD-ROM together

The book has fifteen key activities, each opening with an introductory 'context' page to set a scene around which the problem-solving activities are based. The activities are presented on three activity sheets, which can be projected on to a whiteboard for whole class use or photocopied/printed for display. Sharing the activities either on screen or paper provides lots of opportunities for discussing the introductory page and the questions posed, encouraging pupils to use and extend their existing mathematical skills and knowledge.

For each context there are three activity sheets at different ability levels to enable teachers to introduce the problem-solving skills in stages. An animal picture at the top of the sheet indicates the level of the activity sheet. The cat exercises are at the simplest level; the dog exercises are at the next level; the rabbit exercises are at the most advanced level. You may decide to give some pupils the cat activity sheet and then decide, on the basis of their success, to ask them to complete the dog activity sheet. A similar approach could be taken with the dog and rabbit sheets.

The teacher should discuss the tasks, ensuring that the children understand clearly how to enjoy the activity and, where appropriate, how to complete the activity sheet. You may wish to guide the pupils with the 'Steps to Success' shown on page 4.

Answers to all the activity sheets can be found on the CD-ROM.

Talk, talk, talk!

The key to success in solving mathematical problems is understanding the vocabulary of the questions posed. High quality discussion, encouraging the children to consider the context and vocabulary as well as number values, will result in much greater confidence and enthusiasm towards maths.

Some of the questions are inevitably quite wordy and complex. Calm, considered reflection about each context and question will take away the fear and panic that often afflicts children in their approach to the subject.

National Curriculum levels

The activity sheets are aimed at the following ability levels:

- **Cat** activity sheets are for pupils working towards Level 2.

- **Dog** activity sheets are for pupils working at Level 2.

- **Rabbit** activity sheets are for pupils who are working confidently at Level 2 and are progressing towards Level 3.

The Steps to Success

 Step 1: Read the problem carefully and check that you understand it.

 Step 2: Look for key facts and numbers in the question.

 Step 3: Choose the operations you are going to use.

 Step 4: Solve the problem and check your answer.

 Step 5: Smile! You have done it!

Andrew Brodie: Improving Problem-solving Skills for ages 7-8 © Bloomsbury Publishing Plc 2013

Ants and spiders

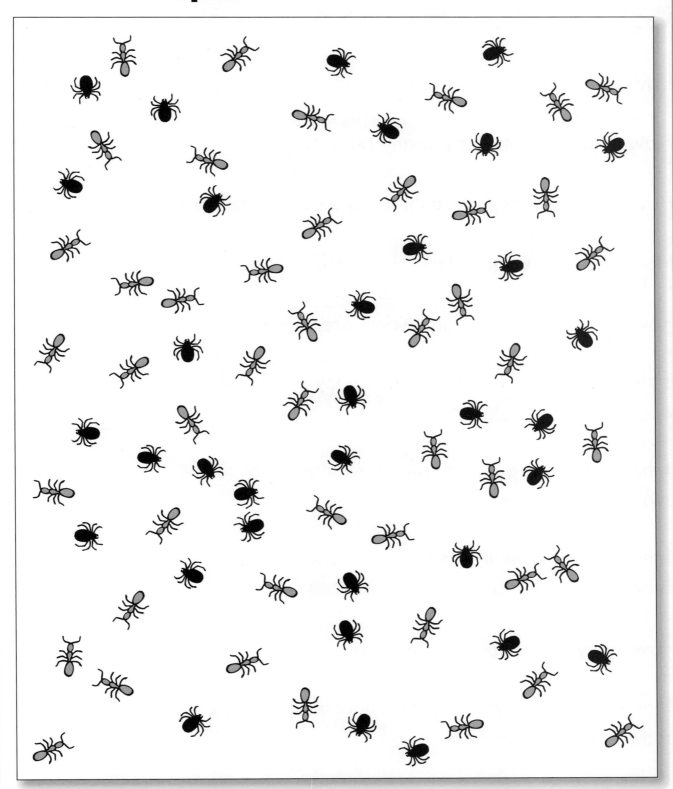

Teacher's notes

Use the illustration as a focus for discussion before using the activity sheets, which follow. Do the children have a strategy for counting the creatures? Ask them to make an estimate of the number of each creature. Comparisons can be made about the creatures' appearance as well as about the number of each type - after all, we are setting out to encourage the children to talk. Do they recognize that each ant has six legs and each spider has eight legs. Remember, talking is key to success in establishing confidence in problem-solving skills.

Ants and spiders

How many ants do you think there are on the page? | [____] ants

Now count the ants. How many are there? | [____] ants

How many spiders do you think there are on the page? | [____] spiders

Now count the spiders. How many are there? | [____] spiders

How many more ants than spiders are there? | [____]

If the ants were put in pairs, how many groups of two would there be? | [____] groups

If the spiders were put in pairs, how many groups of two would there be? | [____] groups

If the ants were put in threes, how many groups of three would there be? | [____] groups

How many ants would be left over? | [____]

If the spiders were put in threes, how many groups of three would there be? | [____] groups

How many spiders would be left over? | [____]

Teacher's notes

Give the children at least one copy each of the context sheet showing a large number of ants and spiders. Can the children count in twos? Do they understand that 'pairs' means the same as 'groups of two'? To find the groups of three, the children might need to draw rings around the creatures.

Andrew Brodie: Improving Problem-solving Skills for ages 7-8 © Bloomsbury Publishing Plc 2013

Ants and spiders

Name _____

Date _____

How many ants do you think there are on the page? [   ] ants

Now count the ants. How many are there? [   ] ants

Was your result more, less or the same as your estimate? [   ]

How much different was it if it was not the same? [   ]

How many more ants would be needed to make
100 altogether? [   ] ants

How many spiders do you think there are on the page? [   ] spiders

Now count the spiders. How many are there? [   ] spiders

Was your result more, less or the same as your estimate? [   ]

How much different was it if it was not the same? [   ]

How many more spiders would be needed to make
100 altogether? [   ] spiders

If the ants were put in fours, how many groups of four
would there be? [   ] groups

How many ants would be left over? [   ]

If the spiders were put in fours, how many groups of
four would there be? [   ] groups

How many spiders would be left over? [   ]

Teacher's notes

Give the children at least one copy each of the context sheet showing a large number of ants and spiders. Can the children count in twos? Do they understand that 'pairs' means the same as 'groups of two'? To find the groups of four, the children may need to draw rings around the creatures.

Ants and spiders

Name _____

Date _____

If the ants were put in fives, how many groups of five would there be?

[   ] groups

How many ants would be left over?

[   ]

How many more ants would be needed to make ten groups of five ants altogether?

[   ] ants

If the spiders were put in fives, how many groups of five would there be?

[   ] groups

How many spiders would be left over?

[   ] spiders

How many more spiders would be needed to make ten groups of five spiders altogether?

[   ] spiders

If the ants were put in eights, how many groups of eight would there be?

[   ] groups

How many ants would be left over?

[   ] ants

How many more ants would be needed to make ten groups of eight ants altogether?

[   ] ants

If the spiders were put in eights, how many groups of eight would there be?

[   ] groups

How many spiders would be left over?

[   ] spiders

How many more spiders would be needed to make ten groups of eight spiders altogether?

[   ] spiders

Teacher's notes

Give the children at least one copy each of the context sheet showing a large number of ants and spiders. To find the groups of five or eight, the children may find it helpful to draw rings around the creatures. For the most able pupils, ask them to calculate the number of ants' legs altogether and the number of spiders' legs altogether. What is the lowest number needed of each type of creature so that the number of legs is the same?

Andrew Brodie: Improving Problem-solving Skills for ages 7-8 © Bloomsbury Publishing Plc 2013

Neighbours

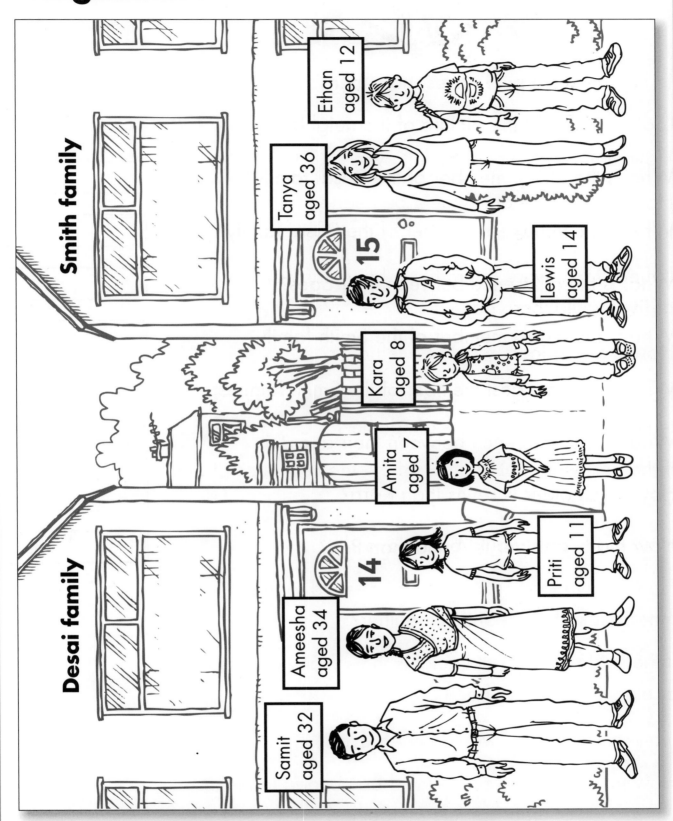

Teacher's notes

Talk about the families: Who is the oldest member of each family? Who is the youngest member of each family? What is the difference between their ages? Do the children know the ages of members of their own families? Talk about the house numbers: Which one is odd? Which one is even?

Name _____

Date _____

Look carefully at the picture of the neighbours.

Who is the oldest member of the Desai family?

Who is the youngest member of the Desai family?

What is the difference between their ages?

Who is the oldest member of the Smith family?

Who is the youngest member of the Smith family?

What is the difference between their ages?

How much older is Lewis than Kara?

How much younger is Amita than Priti?

Teacher's notes

Ensure that the children have the context sheet to refer to. Talk about the families and the ages of the family members. Ensure that the children understand the vocabulary of the questions: this is the key to success in problem-solving. You may also wish to discuss the house numbers shown on the context sheet in relation to odd and even numbers.

Andrew Brodie: Improving Problem-solving Skills for ages 7-8 © Bloomsbury Publishing Plc 2013

Neighbours

Look carefully at the picture of the neighbours.

Who is the oldest person in the two families?

Who is the youngest person in the two families?

What is the difference in their ages?

Who is the oldest child?

How much older than Amita is he?

How much younger than Samit is Amita?

How much younger than her mother is Kara?

Write the names of the people in age order. Start with the youngest.

youngest

oldest

Teacher's notes

Ensure that the children have the context sheet to refer to. Talk about the families and the ages of the family members. Ensure that the children understand the vocabulary of the questions: this is the key to success in problem-solving. You may also wish to discuss the house numbers shown on the context sheet in relation to odd and even numbers.

Neighbours

Look carefully at the picture of the neighbours.

What is the difference in age between the children in the Desai family?

What is the age difference between the oldest and the youngest child in the Smith family?

How much younger than Samit is Amita?

How much older is Tanya than Lewis?

How old was Samit when Priti was born?

One of the houses has an odd number.
What is the number of that house?

Write the number of the house with the even number.

Write all the odd numbers less than 20.

Write all the even numbers less than 20.

Teacher's notes
Ensure that the children have the context sheet to refer to. Talk about the families and the ages of the family members. Ensure that the children understand the vocabulary of the questions: this is the key to success in problem-solving.

I think of a number: addition and subtraction

I think of a number. I add 7.
The answer is 10.
What number did I think of?

I think of a number. I subtract 10. The answer is 13. What number did I think of?

I think of a number. I subtract 4. The answer is 8.
What number did I think of?

I think of a number. I add 30.
The answer is 48.
What number did I think of?

I think of a number. I add 10.
The answer is 17.
What number did I think of?

I think of a number. I subtract 20. The answer is 21. What number did I think of?

Teacher's notes

Use these examples as a focus for discussion before using the activity sheets, which follow. 'Word problems' such as these can be very challenging for some children: help them to understand the question and encourage them to realize that they have to 'work backwards' – ie to 'undo' an addition they need to subtract, or to 'undo' a subtraction they need to add.

Some children will find it very helpful to relate the questions to practical situations: eg, I had a certain number of sweets, I ate four of them; I now have eight sweets. How many did I have to start with?

I think of a number: addition and subtraction

I think of a number. I add 2. The answer is 8. What number did I think of?

I think of a number. I add 6. The answer is 14. What number did I think of?

I think of a number. I subtract 3. The answer is 5. What number did I think of?

I think of a number. I subtract 7. The answer is 8. What number did I think of?

I think of a number. I add 7. The answer is 9. What number did I think of?

I think of a number. I add 8. The answer is 19. What number did I think of?

I think of a number. I subtract 4. The answer is 6. What number did I think of?

I think of a number. I subtract 4. The answer is 18. What number did I think of?

I think of a number. I add 5. The answer is 13. What number did I think of?

I think of a number. I add 10. The answer is 15. What number did I think of?

Teacher's notes
Help the children to read the word problems and to realize that they have to 'work backwards' – ie to 'undo' an addition they need to subtract, or to 'undo' a subtraction they need to add.

Andrew Brodie: Improving Problem-solving Skills for ages 7-8 © Bloomsbury Publishing Plc 2013

I think of a number: addition and subtraction

I think of a number. I add 9. The answer is 14. What number did I think of?

I think of a number. I add 40. The answer is 92. What number did I think of?

I think of a number. I subtract 6. The answer is 7. What number did I think of?

I think of a number. I subtract 30. The answer is 67. What number did I think of?

I think of a number. I add 10. The answer is 16. What number did I think of?

I think of a number. I add 26. The answer is 70. What number did I think of?

I think of a number. I subtract 10. The answer is 24. What number did I think of?

I think of a number. I subtract 19. The answer is 52. What number did I think of?

I think of a number. I add 20. The answer is 35. What number did I think of?

I think of a number. I add 34. The answer is 100. What number did I think of?

Teacher's notes

Remind the children that they have to 'work backwards' – ie to 'undo' an addition they need to subtract, or to 'undo' a subtraction they need to add. Some children will find it very helpful to relate the questions to practical situations: eg, I had a certain number of sweets. I ate six of them. I now have seven sweets. How many did I have to start with?

Name _____

Date _____

I think of a number. I add 9. The answer is 32. What number did I think of?

I think of a number. I add 56. The answer is 81. What number did I think of?

I think of a number. I subtract 8. The answer is 56. What number did I think of?

I think of a number. I subtract 48. The answer is 88. What number did I think of?

I think of a number. I add 20. The answer is 87. What number did I think of?

I think of a number. I add 47. The answer is 121. What number did I think of?

I think of a number. I subtract 40. The answer is 39. What number did I think of?

I think of a number. I subtract 67. The answer is 49. What number did I think of?

I think of a number. I add 27. The answer is 108. What number did I think of?

I think of a number. I add 112. The answer is 240. What number did I think of?

Teacher's notes
Remind the children that they have to 'work backwards' – ie to 'undo' an addition they need to subtract, or to 'undo' a subtraction they need to add.

Andrew Brodie: Improving Problem-solving Skills for ages 7-8 © Bloomsbury Publishing Plc 2013

I think of a number: multiplication and division

I think of a number. I multiply by 2. The answer is 8. What number did I think of?

I think of a number. I divide by 3. The answer is 4. What number did I think of?

I think of a number. I divide by 2. The answer is 6. What number did I think of?

I think of a number. I multiply by 4. The answer is 28. What number did I think of?

I think of a number. I multiply by 5. The answer is 20. What number did I think of?

I think of a number. I divide by 4. The answer is 6. What number did I think of?

I think of a number. I divide by 5. The answer is 6. What number did I think of?

I think of a number. I multiply by 10. The answer is 70. What number did I think of?

I think of a number. I multiply by 3. The answer is 18. What number did I think of?

I think of a number. I divide by 10. The answer is 3. What number did I think of?

Teacher's notes

Use these examples as a focus for discussion before using the activity sheets, which follow. 'Word problems' such as these can be very challenging for some children: help them to understand the question and encourage them to realize that they have to 'work backwards' – ie to 'undo' a multiplication they need to divide, or to 'undo' a division they need to multiply. Some children will find it very helpful to relate the questions to practical situations: eg, I had a certain number of sweets. I shared them with two other people; I now have four sweets. How many did I have to start with?

Andrew Brodie: Improving Problem-solving Skills for ages 7-8 © Bloomsbury Publishing Plc 2013

Name _____

Date _____

I think of a number. I multiply by 2. The answer is 6. What number did I think of?

I think of a number. I multiply by 5. The answer is 50. What number did I think of?

I think of a number. I divide by 2. The answer is 4. What number did I think of?

I think of a number. I divide by 5. The answer is 5. What number did I think of?

I think of a number. I multiply by 2. The answer is 16. What number did I think of?

I think of a number. I multiply by 10. The answer is 60. What number did I think of?

I think of a number. I divide by 2. The answer is 10. What number did I think of?

I think of a number. I divide by 10. The answer is 4. What number did I think of?

I think of a number. I multiply by 5. The answer is 35. What number did I think of?

I think of a number. I multiply by 10. The answer is 90. What number did I think of?

Teacher's notes

Help the children to read the word problems and to realize that they have to 'work backwards' – ie to 'undo' a multiplication they need to divide, or to 'undo' a division they need to multiply.

Andrew Brodie: Improving Problem-solving Skills for ages 7-8 © Bloomsbury Publishing Plc 2013

I think of a number: multiplication and division

I think of a number. I multiply by 2. The answer is 24. What number did I think of?

I think of a number. I multiply by 4. The answer is 32. What number did I think of?

I think of a number. I divide by 2. The answer is 15. What number did I think of?

I think of a number. I divide by 4. The answer is 6. What number did I think of?

I think of a number. I multiply by 2. The answer is 42. What number did I think of?

I think of a number. I multiply by 8. The answer is 72. What number did I think of?

I think of a number. I divide by 2. The answer is 45. What number did I think of?

I think of a number. I divide by 8. The answer is 6. What number did I think of?

I think of a number. I multiply by 3. The answer is 27. What number did I think of?

I think of a number. I multiply by 10. The answer is 120. What number did I think of?

Teacher's notes

Remind the children that they have to 'work backwards' – ie to 'undo' a multiplication they need to divide, or to 'undo' a division they need to multiply.

I think of a number: multiplication and division

I think of a number. I multiply by 2. The answer is 56. What number did I think of?

I think of a number. I multiply by 4. The answer is 52. What number did I think of?

I think of a number. I divide by 2. The answer is 35. What number did I think of?

I think of a number. I divide by 4. The answer is 15. What number did I think of?

I think of a number. I multiply by 2. The answer is 108. What number did I think of?

I think of a number. I multiply by 5. The answer is 90. What number did I think of?

I think of a number. I divide by 2. The answer is 56. What number did I think of?

I think of a number. I divide by 5. The answer is 15. What number did I think of?

I think of a number. I multiply by 3. The answer is 36. What number did I think of?

I think of a number. I multiply by 10. The answer is 540. What number did I think of?

Teacher's notes

Remind the children that they have to 'work backwards' – ie to 'undo' a multiplication they need to divide, or to 'undo' a division they need to multiply. Note that many of the questions on this activity sheet deal with numbers beyond the traditional multiplication tables: pupils will need to logic and number skills to find the missing numbers.

Andrew Brodie: Improving Problem-solving Skills for ages 7-8 © Bloomsbury Publishing Plc 2013

Collecting cards

Ivan has 64
animal cards.

Ethan has 47
animal cards.

Olivia has 58
animal cards.

Jade has 96
animal cards.

Teacher's notes

Encourage the children to talk about the picture in as much detail as possible: How many children are there? Who has the most cards? Who has the least number of cards? How many more cards does Ivan have than Ethan? How many more cards does Ivan have than Olivia? How many animal cards are there altogether?

Collecting cards

Name _____

Date _____

Ivan has 64 animal cards.

Olivia has 58 animal cards.

Jade has 96 animal cards.

Ethan has 47 animal cards.

Who has the most cards?

Who has the fewest cards?

How many more cards has Olivia got than Ethan?

How many more cards has Jade got than Olivia?

How many more cards has Ivan got than Ethan?

If Ethan gave all his cards to Ivan, how many cards would Ivan have?

Teacher's notes

Encourage the children to talk about the picture in as much detail as possible: How many children are there? Who has the most cards? Who has the least number of cards?
Help the children to read the questions on the activity sheet, ensuring that they understand the vocabulary

Andrew Brodie: Improving Problem-solving Skills for ages 7-8 © Bloomsbury Publishing Plc 2013

Collecting cards

Ivan has 64
animal cards.

Olivia has 58
animal cards.

Jade has 96
animal cards.

Ethan has 47
animal cards.

How many more cards has Olivia got than Ethan? ☐

How many more cards has Jade got than Ethan? ☐

How many more cards has Jade got than Olivia? ☐

How many animal cards do the four children
have altogether? ☐

How many more cards would each child need to have 100 cards each?

Ivan would need ☐ cards. Ethan would need ☐ cards.

Olivia would need ☐ cards. Jade would need ☐ cards.

Teacher's notes

Encourage the children to talk about the picture in as much detail as possible: How many children are there? Who
has the most cards? Who has the least number of cards?
Help the children to read the questions on the activity sheet, ensuring that they understand the vocabulary.

Name _____

Date _____

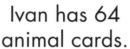

Ivan has 64 animal cards.

Olivia has 58 animal cards.

Jade has 96 animal cards.

Ethan has 47 animal cards.

How many animal cards do the four children have altogether?

If Ivan collected 27 extra cards, how many cards would he have altogether?

If Ethan collected 34 extra cards, how many cards would he have altogether?

If Olivia collected 57 extra cards, how many cards would she have altogether?

If Jade had 25 extra cards, how many cards would she have altogether?

Who would have the most cards now?

How many cards would there be altogether now?

How many more cards would be needed to make a total of one thousand?

Teacher's notes

Encourage the children to talk about the picture in as much detail as possible: How many children are there? Who has the most cards? Who has the least number of cards?
Help the children to read the questions on the activity sheet, ensuring that they understand the vocabulary.

Andrew Brodie: Improving Problem-solving Skills for ages 7-8 © Bloomsbury Publishing Plc 2013

How much change?

58p

86p

75p

62p   100g

Teacher's notes

Talk about each item, ensuring that the children know what each one is and how much it costs. Which is the most expensive? Which is the cheapest? If I have £1 to spend, what change would I have if I bought the Venus Bar? The bottle of water? The crisps? The apple?

Andrew Brodie: Improving Problem-solving Skills for ages 7-8 © Bloomsbury Publishing Plc 2013

How much change?

58p VENUS BAR

86p WATER

62p Crisps 100g cheese

75p

I have £1. If I buy a Venus Bar, how much change do I get?

I have £1. If I buy the bottle of water, how much change do I get?

I have £1. If I buy the crisps, how much change do I get?

I have £1. If I buy the apple, how much change do I get?

I have 50p. If I want to buy the bottle of water, how much more money do I need?

If I buy the Venus Bar and the bottle of water, how much would that cost?

What would be the change from £2?

Teacher's notes

Talk about each item, ensuring that the children know what each one is and how much it costs. Which is the most expensive? Which is the cheapest? Discuss the questions with the children, ensuring that they understand each one, as the question sentences are quite complex. Examine their answers carefully: when finding the change from £1 when buying the crisps, for example, many children will give the answer 48p rather than 38p. They have subtracted the 60p to find 40p but then use their knowledge that 10 - 2 = 8, rather than proceeding to subtract the 2p.

How much change?

58p — VENUS BAR

75p — apple

86p — WATER

Crisps 100g cheese — 62p

Grace has £2. If she buys a Venus Bar, how much change does she get?

If she buys the bottle of water and the crisps, how much would that cost?

What would be the change from £2?

Tom has £2. If he buys the apple, how much change does he get?

If he buys the water instead, how much change does he get?

If he buys the crisps, how much change does he get?

If he buys the Venus Bar and the water, how much does he spend?

How much change would he have from £2?

Will has £2. How much more money would he need if he wanted to buy all four of the items?

Teacher's notes

Talk about each item, ensuring that the children know what each one is and how much it costs. Which is the most expensive? Which is the cheapest? Discuss the questions with the children, ensuring that they understand each one as the question sentences are quite complex.

Andrew Brodie: Improving Problem-solving Skills for ages 7-8 © Bloomsbury Publishing Plc 2013

Name _____

Date _____

58p

75p

86p

62p

Isla has £2.50.

How much money would she have left if she bought the Venus Bar?

How much money would she have left if she bought the bottle of water instead?

How much change would she have if she bought the crisps instead?

How much change would she have if she bought the apple instead?

Can she afford to buy all four items?

How much more money would she need?

On a separate sheet of paper, work out how many different combinations of three items Isla could buy. What would each of these combinations cost?

Work out how much money Isla would have left from her £2.50 if she bought each of the combinations.

Teacher's notes
Discuss the questions with the children, ensuring that they understand each one. Are they aware of what they need to do to find the combinations of three items?

Andrew Brodie: Improving Problem-solving Skills for ages 7-8 © Bloomsbury Publishing Plc 2013

What time is it?

What time does the clock show?

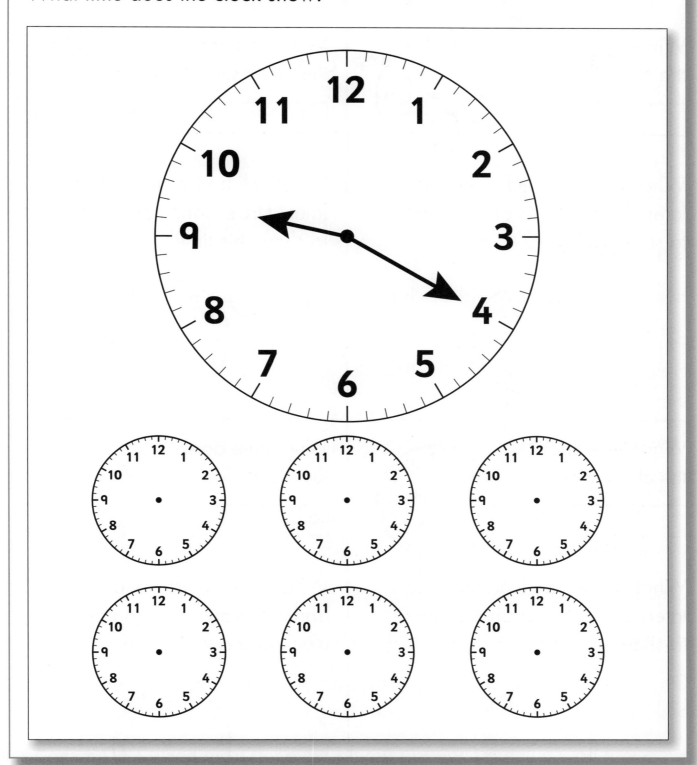

Teacher's notes

Talk about the clock, ensuring that the children can identify the time of twenty past nine. Ask the children what the time will be one hour later: can they show this on one of the blank clock faces? Discuss what the time will be two hours later, three hours later, etc. Discuss what the time was one hour earlier, two hours earlier, etc. Discuss what the time will be half an hour later, etc. How many minutes would it be till ten o'clock? What will the time be half an hour later? A quarter of an hour later?

What time is it?

What time does the clock show?

What will the time be one hour later? Draw hands on the clock to show this time.

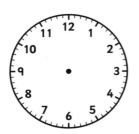

What time does the clock show?

What will be the time one hour later? Draw hands on the clock to show this time.

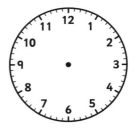

What time does the clock show?

What will be the time one hour later? Draw hands on the clock to show this time.

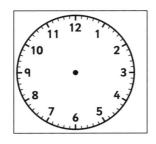

What time does the clock show?

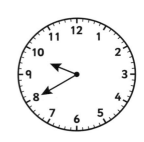

What was the time one hour earlier? Draw hands on the clock to show this time.

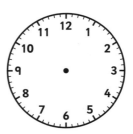

Teacher's notes

Talk about the sheet, ensuring that the children understand what they need to do. Can they correctly identify the hour hand and the minute hand?

What time is it?

Name _____

Date _____

What time does each clock show?

What will the time be half an hour later?

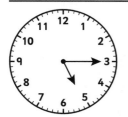

What will be the time forty-five minutes later?

What will be the time forty minutes later?

What will be the time forty-five minutes later?

What will the time be twenty-five minutes later?

What will be the time twenty minutes later?

What will be the time forty minutes later?

What will be the time fifty minutes later?

Teacher's notes

Talk about the sheet, ensuring that the children understand what they need to do. Can they correctly identify the hour hand and the minute hand?

Andrew Brodie: Improving Problem-solving Skills for ages 7-8 © Bloomsbury Publishing Plc 2013

What time is it?

What time does each clock show?

[ ]

What will the time be three and a half hours later?

[ ]

[ ]

What will the time be two and a quarter hours later?

[ ]

[ ]

What will be the time one hour and forty minutes later?

[ ]

[ ]

What will be the time two hours and twenty minutes later?

[ ]

[ ]

What will be the time one hour and ten minutes later?

[ ]

[ ]

What will be the time five and a quarter hours later?

[ ]

[ ]

The cooker timer is set for two hours and twenty-five minutes. At what time will it be ready?

[ ]

[ ]

A film is just starting. The film is one hour and thirty-five minutes long. At what time will it finish?

[ ]

Teacher's notes

Talk about the sheet, ensuring that the children understand what they need to do. Check that they understand that the start times for the cooker timer and the film are represented by the clock faces shown.

Andrew Brodie: Improving Problem-solving Skills for ages 7-8 © Bloomsbury Publishing Plc 2013

What time is it? Roman numerals

What time does the clock show?

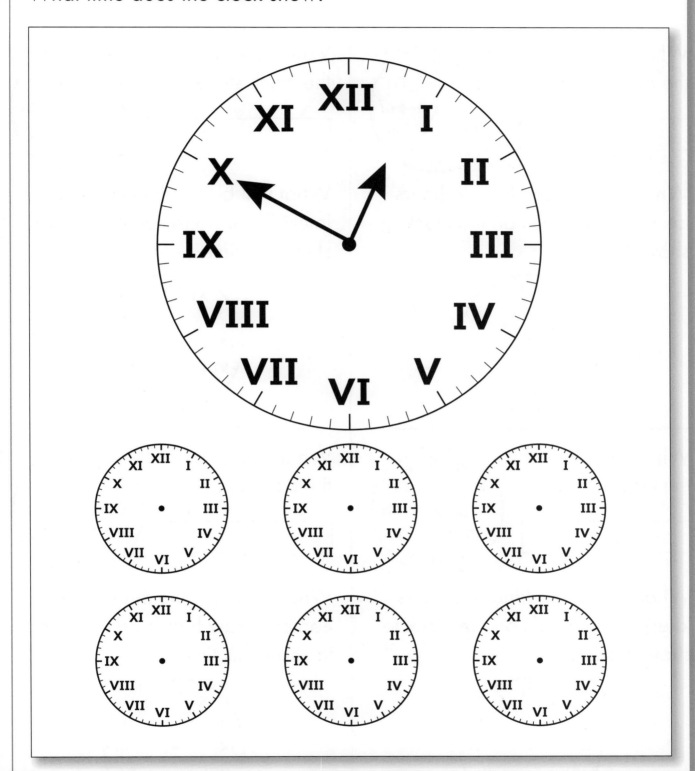

Teacher's notes

Talk about the clock, ensuring that the children can identify the time of ten to one. Do they recognise the Roman numerals? If possible, show them some clocks or watch faces with Roman numerals. Note that some timepieces show the number 4 as IV and some show it as IIII. Do they understand why it could be shown as IV?

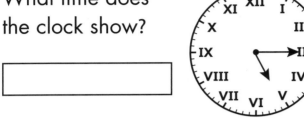

What time is it?

Name _____

Date _____

What time does
the clock show?

[_____]

What will the time be two hours
later? Draw hands on the clock to
show this time.

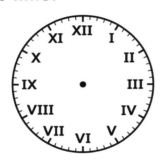

What time does
the clock show?

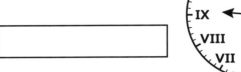

[_____]

What will be the time three hours
later? Draw hands on the clock to
show this time.

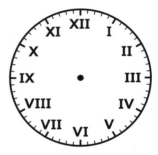

What time does
the clock show?

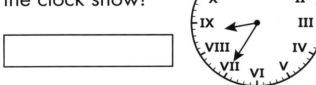

[_____]

What will be the time two hours
later? Draw hands on the clock to
show this time.

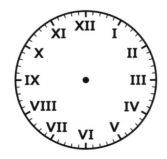

What time does
the clock show?

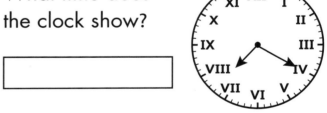

[_____]

What was the time three hours
earlier? Draw hands on the clock
to show this time.

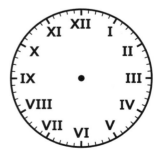

Teacher's notes

Talk about the sheet, ensuring that the children understand what they need to do. Can they correctly identify the
Roman numerals?

Andrew Brodie: Improving Problem-solving Skills for ages 7-8 © Bloomsbury Publishing Plc 2013

What time is it?

Name _____

Date _____

What time does each clock show?

[   ]

What will the time be one hour and five minutes later?

[   ]

[   ]

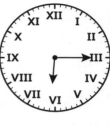

What will the time be one hour and forty-five minutes later?

[   ]

[   ]

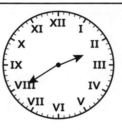

What will be the time one hour and twenty minutes later?

[   ]

[   ]

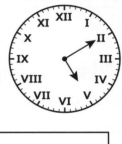

What will be the time one hour and fifty minutes later?

[   ]

[   ]

What will be the time one hour and fifty-five minutes later?

[   ]

[   ]

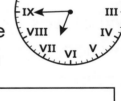

What will be the time two hours and fifteen minutes later?

[   ]

[   ]

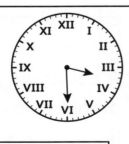

What will be the time four hours and thirty minutes later?

[   ]

[   ]

What will be the time three hours and fifty minutes later?

[   ]

Teacher's notes

Talk about the sheet, ensuring that the children understand what they need to do. Can they correctly identify the Roman numerals? Encourage them to approach the problems in stages: for example, for the first question, they could work out the time one hour later, then five minutes after that.

What time is it?

What time does each clock show?

[_____]	[_____]
What was the time two and a quarter hours earlier?	What was the time one and a half hours earlier?
[_____]	[_____]

[_____]	[_____]
What was the time one and a quarter hours earlier?	What was the time three and a half hours earlier?
[_____]	[_____]

[_____]	[_____]
What was the time an hour and a half earlier?	What was the time two hours and twenty minutes earlier?
[_____]	[_____]

[_____]	[_____]
What was the time an hour and a half earlier?	A television programme is just finishing. It started at 4.55. How long was the programme?
[_____]	[_____]

Teacher's notes

Talk about the sheet, ensuring that the children understand what they need to do. Encourage them to approach the problems in stages: for example, for the first question, they could work out the time two hours earlier, then fifteen minutes before that.

     Andrew Brodie: Improving Problem-solving Skills for ages 7-8 © Bloomsbury Publishing Plc 2013

Months of the year

January has 31 days.

February usually has 28 days but it has 29 in a leap year.

March has 31 days.

April has 30 days.

May has 31 days.

June has 30 days.

July has 31 days.

August has 31 days.

September has 30 days.

October has 31 days.

November has 30 days.

December has 31 days.

Teacher's notes

Talk about the months of the year. What month is it now? What month was it last month? What will next month be? Use ordinal numbers: ie, the first month, the second month, etc.

Months of the year

Name _____

Date _____

Word Bank

January	April	July	October
February	May	August	November
March	June	September	December

What is the first month of the year? ☐

What is the third month of the year? ☐

What is the fourth month of the year? ☐

What is the ninth month of the year? ☐

What is the tenth month of the year? ☐

What is the twelfth month of the year? ☐

Which months have thirty-one days?

☐ ☐ ☐ ☐

☐ ☐ ☐

Which months have thirty days?

☐ ☐ ☐ ☐

Which month does not have 30 or 31 days? ☐

Teacher's notes
Ensure that the children have the context sheet to refer to. This activity sheet will help them to revise their knowledge of ordinal numbers as well as of the months of the year.

Andrew Brodie: Improving Problem-solving Skills for ages 7-8 © Bloomsbury Publishing Plc 2013

Months of the year

Word Bank

January	April	July	October
February	May	August	November
March	June	September	December

What is the first month of the year? ⬜

What is the second month of the year? ⬜

What is the third month of the year? ⬜

How many days are there altogether in the first three months of the year? (When it is not a leap year.) ⬜

What is the fourth month of the year? ⬜

What is the fifth month of the year? ⬜

What is the sixth month of the year? ⬜

How many days are there altogether in the second three months of the year? ⬜

How many days are there altogether in the first six months of the year? (When it is not a leap year.) ⬜

Teacher's notes

Ensure that the children have the context sheet to refer to. This activity sheet will help them to revise their knowledge of ordinal numbers as well as of the months of the year. Note that the vocabulary is complicated by the use of ordinal numbers to refer to sets of three months: ie, the second three months of the year.

Andrew Brodie: Improving Problem-solving Skills for ages 7-8 © Bloomsbury Publishing Plc 2013

Months of the year

Name _____

Date _____

How many days are there altogether in the first three months of the year? (When it is not a leap year.)

[   ] days

How many days are there altogether in the second three months of the year?

[   ] days

How many days are there altogether in the first six months of the year? (When it is not a leap year.)

[   ] days

How many days are there altogether in the third three months of the year?

[   ] days

How many days are there altogether in the last three months of the year?

[   ] days

How many days are there altogether in the second six months of the year?

[   ] days

How many days are there altogether in one year? (When it is not a leap year.)

[   ] days

What month comes four months before May?

[   ]

What month comes seven months after September?

[   ]

What month comes six months before February?

[   ]

Teacher's notes

Ensure that the children have the context sheet to refer to. This activity sheet will help them to revise their knowledge of ordinal numbers as well as of the months of the year. Note that the vocabulary is complicated by the use of ordinal numbers to refer to sets of three months: ie, the second three months of the year.

Andrew Brodie: Improving Problem-solving Skills for ages 7-8 © Bloomsbury Publishing Plc 2013

Pictogram

The children counted the number of birds visiting the bird table in five-minute intervals. For every bird they saw they stuck a picture of a bird on a pictogram.

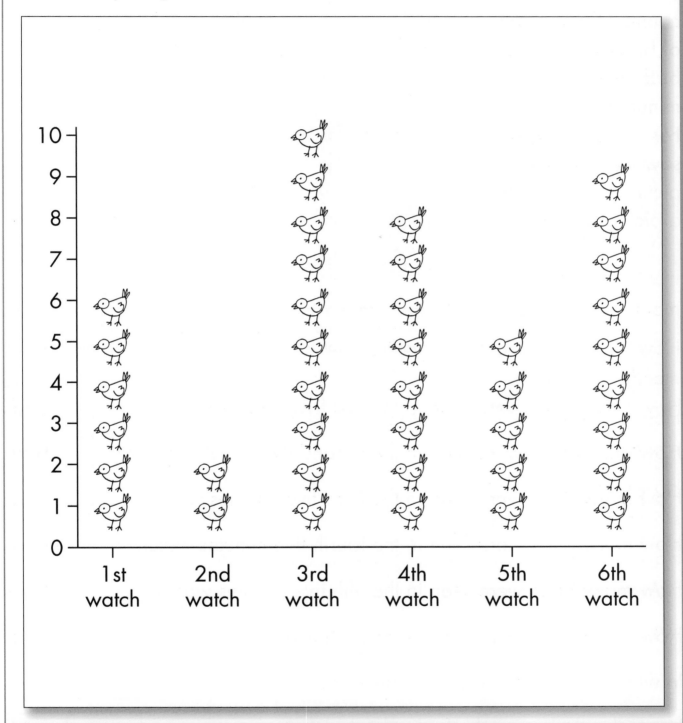

Teacher's notes

Talk about the pictogram, ensuring the children understand how it is calibrated. Do they realise that each 'watch' is for a five-minute interval? If possible, arrange a similar set of watches for the birds visiting a school bird table.

Andrew Brodie: Improving Problem-solving Skills for ages 7-8 © Bloomsbury Publishing Plc 2013

Pictogram

The children counted the number of birds visiting the bird table in five-minute intervals. For every bird they saw they stuck a picture of a bird on a pictogram.

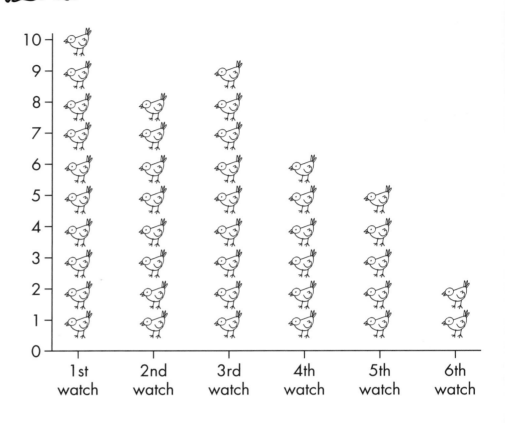

How many birds were seen in the first five minutes watch? ☐ birds

How many birds were seen in the second five minutes watch? ☐ birds

How many birds were seen in the third five minutes watch? ☐ birds

How many birds were seen in the fourth five minutes watch? ☐ birds

How many birds were seen in the fifth five minutes watch? ☐ birds

How many birds were seen in the sixth five minutes watch? ☐ birds

In which watch were the most birds seen? ☐ watch

In which watch were the fewest birds seen? ☐ watch

Teacher's notes

Ensure that the children understand how to interpret the chart. Do they understand the questions? Note the use of ordinal numbers: 1st, 2nd, 3rd, 4th, 5th, 6th.

Andrew Brodie: Improving Problem-solving Skills for ages 7-8 © Bloomsbury Publishing Plc 2013

Pictogram

Name _____

Date _____

The children counted the number of birds visiting the bird table in five-minute intervals. For every bird they saw they stuck a picture of a bird on a pictogram.

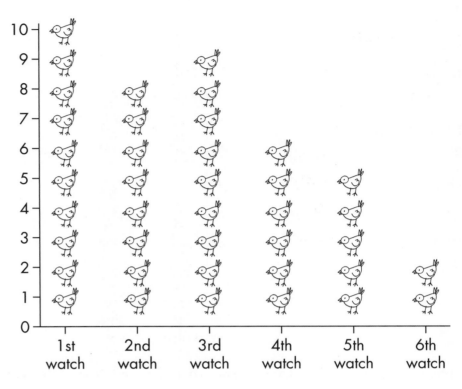

How many more birds were seen in the first five minute watch than in the second five minute watch?   ☐ birds

How many fewer birds were seen in the second five minute watch than in the third five minute watch?   ☐ birds

How many more birds were seen in the third five minute watch than in the fourth five minute watch?   ☐ birds

How many fewer birds were seen in the fifth five minute watch than in the first five minute watch?   ☐ birds

How many more birds were seen in the second five minute watch than in the sixth five minute watch?   ☐ birds

Teacher's notes
Ensure that the children understand how to interpret the chart. Do they understand the questions? Note the use of ordinal numbers: 1st, 2nd, 3rd, 4th, 5th, 6th.

Pictogram

The children counted the number of birds visiting the bird table in five-minute intervals. For every bird they saw they stuck a picture of a bird on a pictogram.

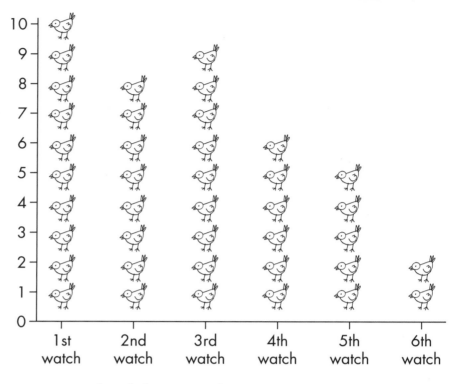

How many birds were seen in each of the watches?

1st watch	2nd watch	3rd watch	4th watch	5th watch	6th watch

Altogether, how many birds were seen in the first ten minutes? ☐ birds

Altogether, how many birds were seen in the middle ten minutes? ☐ birds

Altogether, how many birds were seen in the final ten minutes? ☐ birds

How many birds were seen altogether in the half hour? ☐ birds

Suggest a reason that more birds were seen in the first ten minutes than in the final ten minutes.

_____

Teacher's notes

Ensure that the children understand how to interpret the chart. Do they understand the questions? Note the use of ordinal numbers: 1st, 2nd, 3rd, 4th, 5th, 6th.

Andrew Brodie: Improving Problem-solving Skills for ages 7-8 © Bloomsbury Publishing Plc 2013

Information in tables

Children in Langford School are allowed to eat one item of fruit each at break time. The tables show the number of pieces of fruit eaten by the children in Classes 1, 2 and 3.

Class 1

Apple	Banana	Orange	Pear
12	4	7	6

Class 2

Apple	Banana	Orange	Pear
5	8	7	4

Class 3

Apple	Banana	Orange	Pear
10	9	2	12

Teacher's notes

Talk about the tables, ensuring that the children understand what they represent. If possible, create some similar tables about items of fruit eaten in your school.

Name _____

Date _____

Children in Langford School are allowed to eat one item of fruit each at break time. Look at the table showing the number of pieces of fruit eaten by the children in Class 1.

Class 1			
Apple	Banana	Orange	Pear
12	4	7	6

Which was the most popular fruit amongst the children of Class 1?

Which was the least popular fruit?

Write the names of the fruits in order of popularity.

How many more apples were eaten than pears?

How many fewer oranges were eaten than apples?

How many pieces of fruit were eaten altogether by the children in Class 1?

Teacher's notes
Ensure that the children understand how to interpret the chart. Do they understand the questions?

Andrew Brodie: Improving Problem-solving Skills for ages 7-8 © Bloomsbury Publishing Plc 2013

Name _____

Date _____

Children in Langford School are allowed to eat one item of fruit each at break time. Look at the table showing the number of pieces of fruit eaten by the children in Class 2.

Class 2			
Apple	Banana	Orange	Pear
5	8	7	4

Which was the most popular fruit amongst the children of Class 2?

How many pieces of fruit were eaten altogether by the children in Class 2?

Now look at the table showing the number of pieces of fruit eaten by the children in Class 1.

Class 1			
Apple	Banana	Orange	Pear
12	4	7	6

How many pieces of fruit were eaten altogether by the children in Class 1?

How many fewer apples were eaten by the children in Class 2 than by the children in Class 1?

How many more bananas were eaten by the children in Class 2 than by the children in Class 1?

Teacher's notes
Ensure that the children understand how to interpret the tables. Do they understand the questions?

Name _____

Date _____

Children in Langford School are allowed to eat one item of fruit each at break time.

Look at the table showing the fruit eaten by the children in Class 3.

What was the most popular fruit?

What was the least popular fruit?

How many children do you think were present in Class 3 on the day of the survey?

Explain your answer on the back of this sheet.

Look at all three tables.

Altogether, how many apples were eaten at break time on the day of the survey?

⬜ apples

Altogether, how many bananas were eaten at break time on the day of the survey?

⬜ bananas

Altogether, how many oranges were eaten at break time on the day of the survey?

⬜ oranges

Altogether, how many pears were eaten at break time on the day of the survey?

⬜ pears

If bananas cost 47p each, what was the total cost of the bananas?

Teacher's notes

Provide the children with a copy of the context sheet, which shows the table of results for each class. Ensure that the children understand how to interpret the tables. Their answer to the question about the number of children present in Class 3 might not be equal to the number of pieces of fruit eaten as some children might not have chosen to eat any. The final question is highly challenging: Can the children find a method to solve it?

Andrew Brodie: Improving Problem-solving Skills for ages 7-8 © Bloomsbury Publishing Plc 2013

Planks of wood

These children have each got a plank of wood.

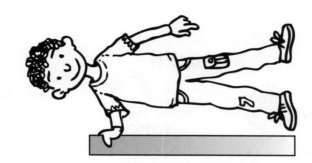

Jack's plank is 112cm long.

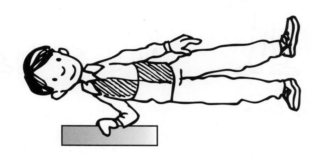

Austin's plank is 52cm long.

Beth's plank is 89cm long.

Amy's plank is 167cm long.

Teacher's notes

Talk about the sizes, perhaps measuring them out on the classroom floor so that the children can visualise the lengths. Discuss who has the longest plank, who has the shortest, how much longer one is than another, how much shorter one is than another, etc.

Planks of wood

Amy

Beth

Austin

Jack

Amy's plank is 167cm long.

Beth's plank is 89cm long.

Austin's plank is 52cm long.

Jack's plank is 112cm long.

Who has the longest plank of wood? ☐

Who has the shortest plank of wood? ☐

How much longer is Beth's plank than Austin's? ☐ cm

How much shorter is Jack's plank than Amy's? ☐ cm

If Beth and Austin join their planks together, will their joined plank be longer or shorter than Amy's? ☐

Will their joined plank be longer or shorter than Jack's? ☐

Teacher's notes

Talk about the sizes, perhaps measuring them out on the classroom floor so that the children can visualise the lengths. Discuss the last two questions, encouraging the children to make comparisons between the lengths of the planks.

Andrew Brodie: Improving Problem-solving Skills for ages 7-8 © Bloomsbury Publishing Plc 2013

Planks of wood

Amy's plank is 167cm long.

Beth's plank is 89cm long.

Austin's plank is 52cm long.

Jack's plank is 112cm long.

How much longer is Amy's plank than Jack's? [ ] cm

How much shorter is Austin's plank than Beth's? [ ] cm

How much longer is Amy's plank than Austin's? [ ] cm

How much shorter is Beth's plank than Jack's? [ ] cm

If Beth and Austin join their planks together, what will be the total length of their wood? [ ] cm

If Amy and Jack join their planks together, what will be the total length of their wood? [ ] cm

What will be the difference in size between the two new lengths of wood? [ ] cm

Teacher's notes

Talk about the sizes, perhaps measuring them out on the classroom floor so that the children can visualise the lengths. Discuss the last question, ensuring that the children understand that it refers to a comparison between the new length of wood created by Beth and Austin and that created by Amy and Jack.

Planks of wood

Name _____

Date _____

Amy's plank is 167cm long.

Beth's plank is 89cm long.

Austin's plank is 52cm long.

Jack's plank is 112cm long.

Amy says they should saw their planks of wood to make them all the same length as Austin's.

How many pieces could Amy make?

How much would she have left over? _____ cm

How many pieces could Beth make?

How much would she have left over? _____ cm

How many pieces could Jack make?

How much would he have left over? _____ cm

If they join their offcuts (the pieces left over) together, how much would need to be sawn off to make another piece the size of Austin's? _____ cm

How many 52cm planks do they now have altogether?

Amy suggests that they join all the planks together side by side to make the base for a den. If each plank is 15cm wide, what would be the total width of the den base? _____ cm

Teacher's notes

Talk about the questions, ensuring that the children are following and understanding the narrative.

Andrew Brodie: Improving Problem-solving Skills for ages 7-8 © Bloomsbury Publishing Plc 2013

Picture tiles

The teacher asks every child in the class to paint a picture on a tile.

Teacher's notes

Choose a size of tile to discuss: for example, each tile could be 12cm square. Ensure the children understand that when we refer to '12cm square', we mean the tile is a square and that each side must be 12cm long. Talk about different arrangements of the tiles. For example, if the tiles are arranged in panels of three in a row, what would be the total length of each panel?

Name _____

Date _____

Picture tiles

The teacher asks every child in the class to paint a picture on a tile.

If each tile is 10cm square, how long is a panel made of two tiles side by side?

[   ] cm

If each tile is 10cm square, how long is a panel made of three tiles in a row?

[   ] cm

How many tiles would be needed to make a row 50cm long?

[   ] tiles

How many tiles would be needed to make a row 80cm long?

[   ] tiles

How many tiles would be needed to make a row 1 metre long?

[   ] tiles

Look at this picture of a panel made from the tiles.

How many centimetres long is the panel?

[   ] cm

How wide is the panel?

[   ] cm

Altogether how many tiles is the panel made of?

[   ] tiles

Teacher's notes

Ensure the children understand that when we refer to '10cm square', we mean the tile is a square and that each side must be 10cm long. Can they work out how to add the 10cm lengths together to find the answers to the questions?

Andrew Brodie: Improving Problem-solving Skills for ages 7-8 © Bloomsbury Publishing Plc 2013

Name _____

Date _____

Picture tiles

The teacher asks every child in the class to paint a picture on a tile.

If each tile is 12cm square, how long is a panel made of two tiles side by side?

☐ cm

If each tile is 12cm square, how long is a panel made of three tiles in a row?

☐ cm

How many tiles would be needed to make a row 60cm long?

☐ tiles

How many tiles would be needed to make a row 84cm long?

☐ tiles

How many tiles would be needed to make a row longer than 1 metre?

☐ tiles

Look at this picture of a panel made from the tiles.

How many centimetres long is the panel?

☐ cm

How wide is the panel?

☐ cm

Teacher's notes

Ensure the children understand that when we refer to 12cm square', we mean the tile is a square and that each side must be 12cm long. Can they work out how to add the 12cm lengths together to find the answers to the questions?

Andrew Brodie: Improving Problem-solving Skills for ages 7-8 © Bloomsbury Publishing Plc 2013

Picture tiles

Name _____

Date _____

The teacher asks every child in the class to paint a picture on a tile.

If each tile is 15cm square, how long is a panel made of two tiles side by side?

[ ] cm

If each tile is 15cm square, how long is a panel made of three tiles in a row?

[ ] cm

How many tiles would be needed to make a row 60cm long?

[ ] tiles

How many tiles would be needed to make a row 105cm long?

[ ] tiles

How many tiles would be needed to make a row longer than 2 metres?

[ ] tiles

Look at the panel above.

How many centimetres long is the panel? [ ] cm

How wide is the panel? [ ] cm

Using the same number of tiles, work out on the back of this sheet the dimensions of two other panels that could be made.

Teacher's notes
Ensure the children understand that when we refer to 15cm square', we mean the tile is a square and that each side must be 15cm long. Can they work out how to add the 15cm lengths together to find the answers to the questions?

Andrew Brodie: Improving Problem-solving Skills for ages 7-8 © Bloomsbury Publishing Plc 2013

Sweets in jars

pineapple chunks

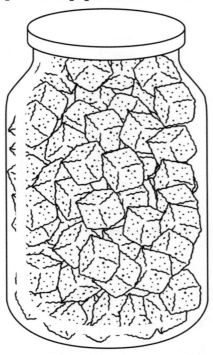

flying saucers

pear drops

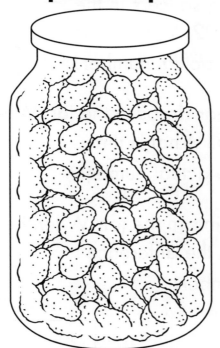

mints

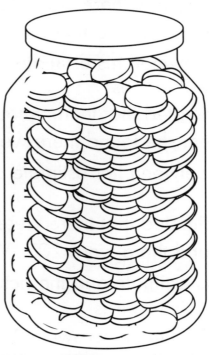

Teacher's notes

If possible, it would be helpful to have at least one jar containing marbles to represent sweets. Ask the children to estimate the number of marbles in the jar, then ask them to count the marbles carefully. Who made the closest estimate to the actual number?

Sweets in jars

| pineapple chunks | flying saucers | pear drops | mints |

Grace estimated that there were 160 pineapple chunks in the jar. When she counted them she found there were only 138. What is the difference between her estimate and the actual number?

Tom estimated that there were 200 flying saucers in the jar. When he counted them he found there were only 92. What is the difference between his estimate and the actual number?

Sammy estimated that there were 86 pear drops in the jar. When she counted them she found there were 125. What is the difference between her estimate and the actual number?

George estimated that there were 46 mints in the jar. When he counted them he found there were 203. What is the difference between his estimate and the actual number?

Which jar had the most sweets?

Of which sweets were there fewest?

Teacher's notes

Help the children to read the questions very carefully. They are very wordy and some children will find difficulty in finding and interpreting the key information.

Andrew Brodie: Improving Problem-solving Skills for ages 7-8 © Bloomsbury Publishing Plc 2013

pineapple chunks

flying saucers

pear drops

mints

Grace estimated that there were 160 pineapple chunks in the jar.

Tom estimated that there were 200 flying saucers in the jar.

Sammy estimated that there were 86 pear drops in the jar.

George estimated that there were 46 mints in the jar.

The children then counted the sweets and made a table of results.

Type of sweet	pineapple chunks	flying saucers	pear drops	mints
Estimated number	160	200	86	46
Actual number	138	92	125	203
Error				

Complete the table by entering the amount of error between each estimate and actual number.

Which child had the smallest error?

Which child's estimate was furthest from the actual number?

How many more pineapple chunks than flying saucers were there?

How many fewer pear drops than mints were there?

Teacher's notes

Help the children to read the questions very carefully. Ensure that they can interpret the table correctly and that they understand how to fill in the missing data.

Andrew Brodie: Improving Problem-solving Skills for ages 7-8 © Bloomsbury Publishing Plc 2013

Sweets in jars

Type of sweet	pineapple chunks	flying saucers	pear drops	mints
Actual number	138	92	125	203

How many sweets are there altogether? [＿＿＿] sweets

Tom suggests that the four children should share out the flying saucers. How many would they have each and
would there be any left over? [＿＿＿] each [＿＿＿] left over

Grace suggests that the four children should share out the pineapple chunks. How many would they have
each and would there be any left over? [＿＿＿] each [＿＿＿] left over

Sammy suggests that the four children should share out the pear drops. How many would they have each and
would there be any left over? [＿＿＿] each [＿＿＿] left over

George suggests that the four children should share out the mints. How many would they have each and
would there be any left over? [＿＿＿] each [＿＿＿] left over

If the children now each have the same number of each
type of sweet, how many sweets would they each have? [＿＿＿] each

Altogether, how many sweets would be left over? [＿＿＿] left over

Teacher's notes
Help the children to read the questions very carefully. They are very wordy and some children will find difficulty in finding and interpreting the key information.

Andrew Brodie: Improving Problem-solving Skills for ages 7-8 © Bloomsbury Publishing Plc 2013

Comparing numbers

Teacher's notes

Talk about the numbers. Which ones are one-digit numbers? Which ones are two-digit? Which ones are three-digit? Which ones are odd? (Nearly all of them!)
Compare the sizes of the numbers. Add some of the numbers together.

Andrew Brodie: Improving Problem-solving Skills for ages 7-8 © Bloomsbury Publishing Plc 2013

Comparing numbers

Look at these numbers.

> 53   19   569   7
>
> 2   913   29   149

Write the one-digit numbers.

Write the two-digit numbers.

Write the three-digit numbers.

Which is the smallest of the numbers?

Which is the biggest of the numbers?

What is the difference between the largest number and the smallest number?

Add the one-digit numbers together.

Subtract 19 from 53.

53 take away 29.

What is the total of 53 and 29?

Teacher's notes
Help the children to read the questions, ensuring that they understand the vocabulary - a critical skill in problem-solving. Can they work out what calculations they need to complete?

Andrew Brodie: Improving Problem-solving Skills for ages 7-8 © Bloomsbury Publishing Plc 2013

Comparing numbers

Look at these numbers.

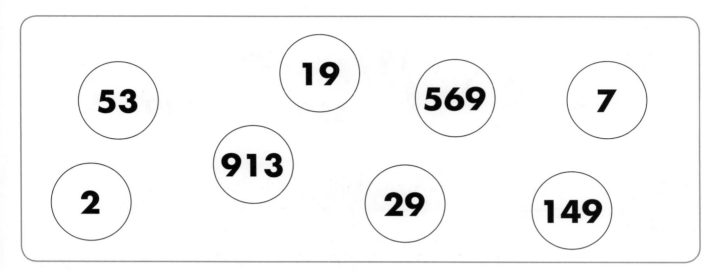

Write the numbers in order of size, starting with the smallest.

smallest

largest

What is the total of 149 and 53?

What is the difference between 149 and 53?

Add the two-digit numbers together.

Add the sum of the one-digit numbers to the sum of the two-digit numbers.

Subtract 19 from 913.

Add 149 to 569.

Multiply each of the two-digit numbers by 2.

Teacher's notes

Help the children to read the questions, ensuring that they understand the vocabulary – a critical skill in problem-solving. Can they work out what calculations they need to complete?

Comparing numbers

Look at these numbers.

53   2   913   19   569   29   149   7

Write the numbers in order of size, starting with the smallest.

smallest [ ] [ ] [ ] [ ]

[ ] [ ] [ ] [ ] **largest**

What is the total of 569 and 149?   [ ]

What is the difference between 913 and 569?   [ ]

Subtract 149 from 913.   [ ]

Multiply 19 by 7.   [ ]

What is 29 times 7?   [ ]

Multiply 53 by 7.   [ ]

Find the sum of the one-digit numbers.   [ ]

What is the total of the two-digit numbers?   [ ]

Add together the three-digit numbers.   [ ]

What is the sum of all the numbers?   [ ]

Teacher's notes

Help the children to read the questions, ensuring that they understand the vocabulary – a critical skill in problem-solving. Can they work out what calculations they need to complete? The multiplication questions may be beyond the scope of the tables the pupils know but can they work out methods to solve them? To answer the final question, do they make use of their previous calculations?

Andrew Brodie: Improving Problem-solving Skills for ages 7-8 © Bloomsbury Publishing Plc 2013